THE LITTLE BOOK OF
IMMORALS

Also by Colin Bowles

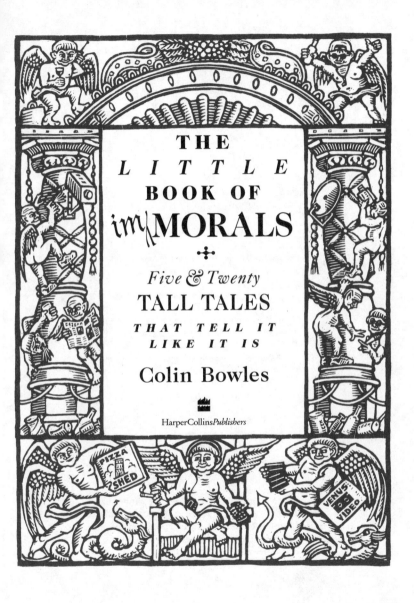

THE *LITTLE* BOOK OF im|MORALS

✦

Five & Twenty
TALL TALES
THAT TELL IT LIKE IT IS

Colin Bowles

HarperCollins*Publishers*

HarperCollins*Publishers*
77–85 Fulham Palace Road,
Hammersmith, London W6 8JB

Published by HarperCollins*Publishers* 1996

1   3   5   7   9   8   6   4   2

A catalogue record for this book is
available from the British Library

ISBN 0 00 638803 5

Photoset in Caslon by
Rowland Phototypesetting Ltd
Bury St Edmunds, Suffolk

Printed and bound in Great Britain

CONTENTS

INTRODUCTION

ONCE UPON A TIME, long ago, there was a fellow called Aesop. He wrote little stories that all started: Once upon a time, long ago . . .

Just like this one did.

These stories helped the average Greek punter of 600 BC work out which way was up. All the tales ended with a moral: a kernel of wisdom that would help the reader find his or her way through life.

Twenty-six centuries later this is a cruel and nasty AIDS-ridden, lawyer-friendly, horrible, cynical little world. After using it as an excuse to murder each other for hundreds of years, most people have finally given up on religion and 'moral' is a dirty word. And yet most of us feel that we need some code, some philosophy to cling to as we slide down the razor blade of life.

Ten years ago, during a condominium redevelopment in Athens, a construction worker discovered a manuscript that contained the work of one of Aesop's contemporaries. Little is known about the author, Beerslop, but the collection of parables and stories – *Beerslop's Fables*, or, as they are better known, *The Little Book of Immorals* – may one day be recognised as a discovery as important as the Dead Sea Scrolls.

The fables were left forgotten in the construction

worker's lunchbox for many years, alongside some pieces of fetta and dried up taramasalata. They were rediscovered by accident during a car-boot sale in Piraeus and purchased by an independent collector. They were brought back to London where they were offered for publication for the first time. They contain what have become known as the Twenty-Five Golden Rules, a distillation of the wisdom of the ancients that is just as relevant today as it was in Beerslop's time.

What you hold in your hand – the one holding the book anyway – is not just the morals of a Greek, but a guidebook to life itself in the 1990s.

Life may never be the same again.

THE TALE OF THE BIG
FAT OLD MAN WHO LIKED
LITTLE CHILDREN

 HIS EYES, HOW they twinkled! His dimples, how merry! His cheeks were like roses, his nose like a cherry! He had a broad face and a little round belly, that shook when he laughed like a bowlful of jelly!

But appearances can be deceptive.

He sat on the papier mâché throne in the grotto, and thought about going berserk with a semi-automatic weapon.

A little girl in a blue frock was pushed into the grotto by her mother. 'Ho, ho, ho,' he said. 'And what's your name, little girl?'

'Karma,' the little girl said.

'Karma,' Santa repeated, sounding a little sour, but by now he was used to dealing with all kinds of ethnics. 'And what's your first name?'

'That is my first name. Karma Tao I-Ching McCrutchley.'

For a moment Santa was speechless. 'Ho, ho, ho,' he said, after a moment. 'And what would you like for Christmas, little girl?'

9

'I want a CD player, a *Sex With Madonna* video, three new pairs of Reeboks and an orgasm.'

Santa stared at her. 'Ho, ho, ho.'

'I mean it.'

'I'll see what I can do.'

As the girl was getting off his lap she leaned forward to whisper in his ear. Santa eagerly bent towards her to catch her words. A secret perhaps? Some redeeming vestige of lost innocence?

'Give me five bucks or I'll tell my mother you interfered with me.'

Santa groaned. 'I never touched you.'

'Who are they going to believe? A fat fifty-seven-year-old retrenched bank clerk doing casual work for a department store or a sweet ten-year-old little girl?' She held out her hand. 'Do you know what they do to paedophiles in prison?'

Santa handed over the money and little Karma slipped away. Santa closed the grotto for the day. He was getting too old for this job. Kids just weren't kids for very long any more.

'Merry fucking Christmas,' he said, kicking a hole in the papier mâché elf, and went home.

Late one foggy Christmas Eve, Santa put all the reindeer in their traces; there was Dasher and Dancer, Prancer and Vixen, Comet and Cupid, and Nigel and his friend Raymond (two little dears he had to call in at the last minute when Donner and Blitzen got a virus that was going round). At the front of the traces was Rudolph, the red-nosed reindeer, who would be guiding the sleigh that night. Behind him was Bruno, the brown-nosed reindeer. He was just as fast as Rudolph, but he couldn't stop as quickly.

The Christmas Fairy was there too, holding a Christmas tree. 'Where would you like me to put this?' she asked Santa.

'I'll come back for it,' Santa said. 'I haven't got room on the sleigh right now.'

Santa set off and made his first landing on the roof of a mock Tudor mansion in a leafy inner suburb, smashing a solar hot water heater and dislodging a satellite dish. As usual there was no chimney, so Santa left his sleigh double-parked in the street next to a BMW and went to let himself in through the back door, after first disengaging the security device.

He looked at the name tag on the sack he was to deliver. 'Karma McCrutchley, aged ten.' The name seemed somehow familiar. As he was walking up the path he stood on a skateboard in the dark and landed on his back. The sack split open on the backsteps.

'Fucking kids,' Santa said softly under his breath. He started to scoop the toys back into the sack. He couldn't believe his eyes. There was a children's video, *What Aladdin Did with his Lamp and some KY Jelly*; a Barbie doll with her own hot tub, miniature love balls and personal vibrator; and a liquorice-flavoured double dong.

'Kids are growing up too fast these days,' Santa muttered to himself.

He expected the house to be in darkness, but it seemed the children were still up. He peered through a door and saw a ten-year-old girl and a twelve-year-old boy checking out the Pamela Anderson page on the Internet.

'Whatever happened to Lego?' Santa thought. He went upstairs and left the sack in the children's bedroom. As he was passing the parents' bedroom he saw something glinting in the moonlight on the dresser. It looked like sleigh tracks. On a vanity mirror. Enchanted, he went in. 'Snow,' he said, astonished.

In someone's bedroom?

'Snow?'

He bent down and sniffed.

'AAAAAAAA – CHOO!'

Suddenly everything was really nice.

He heard the children running up the stairs. They must have heard him sneeze. He opened the window and jumped through the rose pink air, floating down into the luminous green hibiscus. He hardly felt a thing when he landed.

Amazing stuff, snow.

When he limped out into the lovely, really nice street – his ankle was a pretty shade of blue but barely hurt at all – some craven bastard had stolen his sleigh and slashed his reindeer's hooves.

'Shit, it wasn't insured,' Santa said.

'I told you to lock it up,' Rudolph said.

'But this is Christmas!'

'But this is the nineties!'

Santa sat down on the kerb and wondered what on

earth he was going to do. There were all the toys for all the little boys and girls in the world – not counting parts of Asia and the Middle East – in that sleigh. If he didn't get them delivered none of them would believe in him any more.

If any still did.

He saw someone coming out of the house across the road. Perhaps someone who had seen what had happened, coming to lend a helping hand?

'What do you think you're doing?'

'Someone stole my . . .'

'What are these bloody things?'

'They're my . . .'

'Look what they're doing to my lawn!'

'I can't help it, I'm . . .'

'This is a registered lawn, you know. You should have those bloody things on a lead!'

'Don't you know who I am?'

'I don't care if you're Father Bloody Christmas, get those fucking things off my grass!'

Santa got as far as the end of the street when he ran into the carol singers. There were more than a dozen of them, shoulder to shoulder right across the footpath.

'We WISH you a Merry Christmas, we WISH you a Merry Christmas, we WISH you a Merry Christmas, and a HAPPY NEW YEAR!' The first one held his hand out. 'That's five pounds.'

'What?' Santa said.

'Five pounds. For the Christmas carol.'

'I haven't got five pounds.'

'Typical. You yuppie bastards all want something for nothing.'

The really nice snow that Santa had sniffed was starting to wear off. His ankle was hurting. 'Someone just stole my . . .'

'Let's get him,' one of the other carol singers said.

They jumped him, tore off his clothes, kicked his ribs in and left him bleeding on the footpath. Then they moved on to the next house. He could hear them singing.

'We WISH you a Merry Christmas, we WISH you a Merry Christmas . . .'

Bleeding and almost naked, Santa staggered to the nearest house. There was loud music thrumming through the windows and Volvos and BMWs were parked up and down the street.

Vampires, supermen and gorillas were going into the house. A fancy dress party. Perhaps he could find a costume for himself.

He steadied himself against the wall for support and made his way around to the back of the house. A gold BMW was parked in the garage and he heard voices coming from inside. He hobbled closer to have a look.

He saw himself – Father Christmas – in the back of the car, talking into a mobile phone while a pretty blonde girl wriggled out of a nun's costume.

'Mister Reynolds? This is Doctor Eion McCrutchley. You came to see me the other day about the lump you found? Yes, Mister Reynolds, I've got some good news and some bad news. The bad news is that the lump is malignant, I'm afraid. The path lab gives you about a week. Ten days, tops. The good news? The good news is I'm just about to screw that new receptionist you commented on the other day ... Mister Reynolds? ... He fucking hung up! Merry fucking Christmas to you too!'

The blonde nun had peeled off her clothes. Eion McCrutchley shucked off the Santa suit, tossed it out of the window and threw himself on top of her.

Santa tiptoed over to the car, picked up the Santa suit, and slipped it on. What a break! He tiptoed away again. Well maybe he'd lost the sleigh but at least he had some clothes to wear.

'Eion! I wondered where you'd gone!'

Santa turned around.

A woman in a black leather bodice and black fish-net stockings, holding a whip, came out of the house and grabbed his arm. 'I've been looking everywhere for you. Now's our chance!'

She pulled him towards the black Saab Turbo that was parked across the driveway. 'God, I've wanted you ever since that first pelvic exam you gave me! I've got the latex gloves and the pencil torch in the glove box. Hurry!'

As soon as they were in the back seat of the Saab the woman with the whip forced him down on his back and straddled him with her knees. 'Say it!'

'Say what?' Santa stammered.

'Say: "*I think it's time for your pap smear.*" God, that gets me so hot!'

'Do you believe in Father Christmas?' Father Christmas said.

'What made you ask that?'

'Oh, no reason.'

'Do I believe in fairy tales? Of course I do. I sell time-shares for a living.'

She put her hand between his legs. Santa gave a yelp of surprise. No one had ever touched him there before. Well, maybe once, when one of the elves had walked between his legs and the feather in his hat had just kind of brushed against him . . . but he'd tried to put that out of his mind for years.

'When was the last time you did this?' she whispered.

'As a rule I only come once a year.'

'I do love a man with self control!'

She started to tear at his clothes, like the carol singers, but less gently. When he was completely naked she tugged at his beard. 'Take this stupid thing off!' she said.

Santa let out a little yelp.

The woman in the black leather bodice froze. 'This is a real beard,' she shrieked. 'You're an impostor!'

'Please don't stop,' Santa whispered, 'this is the best Christmas I've ever had!'

The woman screamed and jumped off him. She slapped him around the face, jabbed the butt end of the whip into his kidneys and yelled 'Rape!'

The next thing Santa knew there was a blue strobe flashing in the street and two policemen were reaching inside the car with handcuffs. One sprayed mace at him while the other put his knee in the middle of Santa's spine and forced his wrists behind his back.

'Bloody old pervert!' one of the policemen shouted.

It wasn't until eleven o'clock on Christmas morning that one of the elves finally arrived to get him out on bail. Santa was limping, he had sprained his ankle jumping out of the McCrutchleys' window the night before. His face was a mass of bruises and three of his ribs were cracked. And his testicles, which hadn't given him any trouble in two thousand years, were starting to play up.

'Merry Christmas,' the elf said, as he led him towards the replacement sleigh.

'Bah – humbug!' Santa said.

When they reached the sleigh, he saw the Christmas Fairy waiting there with her Christmas tree.

'Where would you like me to put this?' she asked Santa.

And he told her.

And that's how the fairy got on top of the Christmas tree.

MORAL:

Believe in nothing.
Trust nobody

THE ELEPHANT
AND THE MOUSE

ONE DAY AN ELEPHANT was walking through the jungle when he heard a little voice crying, 'Help me! Help me!' He looked around and saw that the cries were coming from the bottom of a hunter's trap. He looked into the hole and saw his friend, Percy the mouse.

'How they hanging, Perce?' the elephant said.

'Not too good, big fella,' Percy said. 'I've been down this hole for about two days and I'm about to become a statistic.'

'Hang in there,' the elephant said, 'I'll get you out.'

He lowered his trunk down the hole and told Percy to grab hold of it. But his trunk wasn't quite long enough. So then he had a better idea. He pulled down his Marks & Spencer Y-fronts and dropped his old fella down the hole. Now he happened to be a particularly well-endowed pachyderm and Percy was able to grab hold of the dangling dork and clamber out.

Percy was very grateful and promised to return the favour one day.

Percy went on to become a property developer and land speculator, like a lot of other dick-grabbers in this world, and bought himself a red Porsche on the proceeds.

One day he was driving through the jungle when he heard a familiar voice trumpeting, 'Help me! Help me!'

Percy stopped the car and discovered his friend, the elephant, trapped down a deep hole.

'Hold on,' Percy shouted. 'I'll get you out.'

'What with?' the elephant said miserably. 'You couldn't knock the chocolate off a cappuccino with your little thing.'

Percy ignored him. He threw his friend a rope, tied the other end of the rope to the back of his Porsche, and towed the elephant out of the hole.

MORAL:

If you've got a red Porsche, you don't need a big penis

THE PRINCESS WITH
THE FLAXEN HAIR

ONCE UPON A TIME there was a beautiful princess with this amazing flaxen hair that flowed right down her back and trailed behind her like a train on a wedding dress. It wasn't natural, of course, she had it specially flaxed by this AC/DC hairdresser in the King's Road. Anyway, that's irrelevant. The point is, she was a top sort, and every prince in the kingdom was trying to get into her pants.

Rapunzel used to spend most of her time at home, washing her hair, blow-drying it and tying it into braids at the back of her head. Her mother used to say to her, 'Rapunzel, you should get out more and let your hair down a bit.'

One day the king rode by on his charger, a black one with a twin exhaust, an expensive sound system and whitewalls. He saw the princess sitting at her window and exclaimed, 'What a glorious vision! I must have her for my very own!'

He stood below her window and shouted, 'Rapunzel, Rapunzel, let down your hair!'

So she did. And the king climbed up her hair as if it was a golden ladder, right to her window.

As you can imagine, Rapunzel was none too happy about this. 'Ker-ist, what were you trying to do, pull all my hair out?' she shouted at him.

The king fell in love with the princess straight away, even though she had a voice like Janet Street-Porter, and he took her back to his castle and imprisoned her in a high tower so that no other man could see her. He idolised her so much he had her likeness cast in bronze, and erected statues of her on marble pedestals all over the kingdom.

This was a satisfactory arrangement for a while, but then the princess got bored and started to complain. 'Why won't you take me out and show me a good time, like in the tampon ads?' she whined. 'You can afford it.'

But the king refused. 'We must love each other from afar,' he told her. 'It's the romantic thing to do. Farewell, my love. I'm off to shoot boars.'

'Remember to duck,' the princess said bitterly.

One day a hard-hearted, but deeply tanned, young man rode into the kingdom. It was a cold, dark knight. He saw the statues of the beautiful princess and said, 'Who is the beautiful maiden with the flax look?'

One of the king's serfs, who wanted the knight to have a square deal (yes, he was a square deal serf), pointed to the distant castle and said, 'She is imprisoned in yonder castle, waiting for a brave knight to come and rescue her.'

'That's me,' the young knight said. 'Lancelot by name, and Lancelot by nature.'

Now you may be asking why the prince did not climb

up Rapunzel's golden tresses like the king did. The fact is, Rapunzel had been having a lot of bad hair days recently and she had decided to go short.

Anyway, Lancelot was a very resourceful young knight. That evening he rode up to the castle in a little van with a red telephone on the top and shouted, 'Medium sized deep-pan pizza with olives and furry fish for the king!'

The drawbridge swung open and he went in. Once inside he went straight to the tower, found the princess, and together they escaped out of the window.

Lancelot took her back to his luxury converted warehouse in an affluent section of Camelot, and after they'd convinced each other that they hadn't slept with any bisexuals or intravenous drug users recently, they bonked their little hearts out. And if they didn't exactly live happily ever after, they were at least reasonably content for quite a long period.

The king was left with just the statues and the deep-pan pizza with anchovies to remind him of Rapunzel. He lost heart with the job, and shortly afterwards was deposed in a bloodless coup.

MORAL:
Men who put women on pedestals
rarely knock them off

THE BEAUTY
AND THE BEAST

ONCE UPON YET ANOTHER TIME there was a beautiful young woman who was trapped in an enchanted castle by a vile and horrible beast. I shan't bore you with the details, it's a long story. Anyway, the beautiful girl wasn't stupid – yes, she was a brunette, and she didn't live in Essex – so she tried to run away. Outside the castle she was immediately attacked by a pack of rabid wolves, some fearsome goblins, and a gang of muggers.

The castle was in Brixton.

Fortunately the Beast had come looking for her, and was on hand to fight off the wolves and the goblins and the muggers, and resuscitate her, and get her to a good hospital, and deal with the media, and pay her medical bills, and generally play the good guy. And Beauty was very grateful.

Then she met Gaston. Gaston was a doctor at the hospital. He pumped iron, and had a mobile phone, and drove a Ferrari with the number plate TESTOST-ERONE. He was shallow and totally self-obsessed and – you guessed it – blond, and he wanted to take Beauty away from the Beast, despite everything the Beast had done for her.

'Beauty,' the vile Beast pleaded, 'I may be cosmetically challenged but I can offer you love and devotion and kindness and understanding and sensitivity. What can Gaston offer you? Just a fantastic body and a chance to gather incredible kudos in front of your friends. Who do you choose?'

And Beauty said, 'I'd still like to be friends, *but . . .*'

MORAL:

Beauty is only skin deep.
But who wants to sleep with
someone with no skin?

Arthur King and
The Nights on
The Round Table

ONCE UPON A TIME in merrye England there was a time of great chaos and suffering and bad fiscal management. (I know you'll find this hard to believe, but bear with me.) And the government of the day was in disarray and all the Lords and the Members got together and said to one another, Whoever can pull this government out of the hole is the rightful leader of the party.

And lo, one day there appeared in their ranks a young man named Arthur King. Arthur was unusual for a politician in that he was bright, attractive, sincere, had good ideas and great charisma. This contrasted markedly with the other leaders of the day and the polls reflected it.

'Where else will we find a man of his calibre?' all the pollsters and government advisers said to each other.

And so Arthur was groomed as heir apparent. The only thing Arthur did not have was a suitable spouse and so he was quickly married off to Guinevere, who made the perfect Tory wife as she was quiet, vacuous and had three small children. Soon afterwards Arthur was voted in as leader of the party and crowned as successor amid the acclamations of the common folk.

One day, sitting at his round table in the cabinet room, Arthur had a vision of the Holy Grail – a knighthood from the queen. He told all his ministers to ride forth and do their utmost to make sure he got one.

From that day on he ruled wisely and justly, righting the wrongs of the poor and bringing peace to all the realm. His fame spread far and wide. When anyone was oppressed by a landlord or the VAT office he would write to Arthur King for help and one of his ministers would ride to the rescue. Their adventures could fill many books. It was regarded as the most glorious era in English history.

Unfortunately the most glorious era in English history lasted about three weeks.

Soon afterwards Arthur King's government was afflicted by the breath of scandal. Lancelot, the minister for defence, was discovered by a photographer from the *Sun* leaving the home of an underwear model at three o'clock in the morning. He decided to leave politics to spend more time with his family. Sir Galahad was charged with an offence involving a jar of yoghurt, a stick of celery and a schoolboy.

Sir Gawain admitted selling arms to the Iraqis.

It was the lead-in to the next election and things looked bad in the polls. The Lords and the party members shook their heads and frowned and wondered what to do about Arthur. He appeared to have lost the plot. 'What are we going to do with a man of his ex-calibre?' they said to each other.

Arthur's opponent, Mordred, was fifteen points ahead

as preferred leader and all looked lost. It was about then that a hand appeared from a lake all clad in white samite – this is Arthur's story anyway – and handed him a brown paper envelope containing photographs and tape recordings that proved that Mordred had once had an affair with Merlin's wife, Vivien. He had been bonking her late at night on the boardroom table and had once taken her for a dirty weekend to his country retreat in the Lake District.

Arthur could see the headlines:

THE LADY OF THE LAKES.

NIGHTS ON THE ROUND TABLE.

When Merlin's wife found out that Arthur was planning to release the story to the press, she came to him and begged him to reconsider. 'It was a long time ago,' she said. 'Merlin doesn't know about it and the shock would kill him. Our marriage is back on track now, we've got back the old magic. Surely you wouldn't wreck my marriage, my career, my family and my reputation just for cheap, short-term political gain?'

Well, I think we all know the answer to that, don't we?

MORAL:

Chivalry is *dead*

THE CAUTIONARY TALE OF
RED RIDING HOOD AND
THE HOUSE OF HORRORS

ONCE UPON A TIME there was a prince and a princess who, after a series of unlikely adventures, got married and lived happily ever after. Or so they thought. But then the children came along and really stuffed things up.

The princess – who after nine months of pregnancy had swollen ankles, post-natal depression and a figure completely shot to hell and had turned into just another tired old queen – gave birth to a baby daughter. They decided to call her Little Red Riding Hood, which was something they found in a book of baby names between 'Letitia' and 'Lola'.

But everyone called her by her second name, Kylie.

Kylie did not grow up to be a kind and sweet little girl, as her parents had imagined. She grew up normal, that is to say a precocious little brat with an opinion about every damned thing. Her mother – who although a kindly soul was by now totally dependent on valium – was always looking for excuses to get her out of the house. She used to send her off to her grandmother's every chance she could.

'Now I don't want to be ageist,' she said to Kylie, 'but the silly old bat can't look after herself any more so you'd better take her over these mung bean sandwiches. And just to be on the safe side, I've put some rubber pants in the basket as well.'

Little Kylie put on her LA Dodgers cap, her ripped jeans and her walkman, jumped on her skateboard, and went off alone through the forest. Now as everyone knows, little girls should not go off alone into the forest these days. The world is full of morally impoverished individuals with difficult to meet needs.

In this case, the Big Bad Wolf. He was wearing a black mackintosh and holding a packet of Smarties.

'Hello, little girl,' he said, 'want a lolly?'

'Get lost, spazzo,' little Kylie told him, being reasonably street-wise for her age. And she headed off as fast as she could.

'Wait,' he shouted after her. 'At least tell me where you're going.'

'I'm going to my grandmother's,' little Kylie shouted back. 'It's pension day and I'm going to rip off her pension cheque before she can get to the letter box.'

For reasons that have never been satisfactorily explained, little Kylie went the long way to her grandmother's house. But the Big Bad Wolf took the short cut, and so he got there before she did. Don't worry too much about this, it's a necessary plot contrivance, as will soon become apparent.

He rapped on the door of Grandma's cottage, which was called, predictably, Dunroamin. Grandma opened the door and saw a big, hairy beast with terrible breath and big teeth and ears.

'Roger,' she said, because not only was she as blind as a bat, she also had Alzheimer's. 'I haven't seen you since Christmas. Did you bring the children?'

The Big Bad Wolf was in no mood to play games. He had just seen *Silence of the Lambs* for the fifteenth time – proving, incidentally, that what people see in the movies and on television *does* affect their behaviour – and he wasted no time in murdering her, stripping her and eating her. Then he put on her clothes – as you have no doubt surmised, he had a lot of deep-seated personal problems, and dressing up in women's clothes was just one of them – jumped into her bed and waited for little Kylie to arrive.

The little girl was absolutely ropeable when she got there. There was no cheque in the mailbox and it seemed as if she had come all that way for nothing.

She opened the door and saw the Big Bad Wolf sitting up in her grandma's bed wearing bedsocks, three Arsenal shirts, her wedding dress and a tea cosy. (Grandma had been trying to keep warm. It was winter and thanks to the caring government of the day, she couldn't afford to pay the electricity bill.)

'Oh Grandma,' little Kylie gasped. 'You smell even worse than usual.'

'It's these rubber pants,' the Big Bad Wolf said.

'And oh, Grandma,' little Kylie said, 'how long since you took your teeth out?'

'They're not that bad,' the Big Bad Wolf said. 'I flossed

after I ate that dead badger I found on the motorway.'

'And oh, Grandma,' little Kylie exclaimed, 'you've got an erection.'

'And a little beauty it is too,' the Big Bad Wolf said. 'Hop in here next to me.'

A short while later the Three Pigs – detectives Silvio Porcini, Frank Bacon and Superintendent Jack Crackling – were on the case. Little Kylie's parents – Mr and Mrs Charming – were in tears, waiting for news of their little daughter.

'Do you think she's all right?' the princess blubbered.

'Well actually,' Superintendent Crackling told her, 'we hold grave fears that she may have been rendered non-viable. We are appealing to the public to come forward with information.'

The Three Pigs got a psychological profile of their suspect from FBI headquarters at Quantico in Virginia and discovered that he was likely to be an involuntarily leisured, economically exploited and underhoused individual with difficult to meet needs. The profile also stated that he was probably ethically disoriented and saw himself as an incomplete success.

This was fascinating, but they had no idea what it all meant.

But a vital breakthrough in the case came on the second day. A kindly wood-cutter was found wandering in the forest near where little Kylie had been reported missing. He was immediately taken to police headquarters with a paper bag over his head to help police with their enquiries.

'Where were you on the day of the fairy story?' Detective Silvio Porcini asked him, after they had roughed him up with some instant coffee in a polystyrene cup and had all smoked several Woodbines in front of him, while typing up the paperwork, thus increasing his risk of contracting lung cancer by passive means.

'I want to see my lawyer,' the kindly wood-cutter said, making the Three Pigs even more suspicious. No one ever wants to talk to a lawyer unless they've got a very good reason – and certainly not at parties.

The Three Pigs got a search warrant and raided the kindly wood-cutter's hut. It was here that they made a crucial discovery – an axe with dried blood stains on the blade.

'My client has no idea how those blood stains got there,' the wood-cutter's lawyer said. 'There is no evidence whatever to connect my client to the alleged crime.'

But a few days later the Three Pigs found two skeletons in a shallow grave in the garden of a nearby cottage. The media had a very hard time deciding how to headline this new and shocking development. They were going to label the case THE HOUSE OF HORRORS but then they realised this had been done before and anyway, the establishment was too small to be called a house. In the end they settled for THE COTTAGE OF CONSTERNATION.

The remains were sent to a forensic laboratory for

testing, where it was discovered that one of the corpses belonged to an animal of the canine species; but the other partly digested corpse was confirmed to be human, and was later identified as Grandma.

She was still wearing her rubber pants.

And so the gentle wood-cutter was found guilty of murder and shortly afterwards hanged himself in prison. His lawyer sued the government for whiplash injuries suffered by his client while in their care – and won. He took the fees for his services out of the dead man's estate and lived happily ever after. (He worked in one of those professions where people actually do live happily for ever, because they can afford to.)

Meanwhile, in an unexpected footnote to the case, the Three Pigs, acting on a tip-off, made their way back to the cottage in the woods. And there they found Grandma sitting up in bed wearing three Arsenal football shirts and bedsocks and the tea cosy and all the rest of it, reading *Cosmopolitan* and stuffing her face with ice cream.

'Oh, Grandma,' Detective Porcini said, 'what lovely smooth skin you've got for a person of your age.'

'That's because I eat a lot of bran.'

'And oh, Grandma,' Detective Bacon said, 'what good eyesight you've got for someone who is really pushing it, if you don't mind me saying.'

'I've got contact lenses in.'

'And oh, Grandma,' Superintendent Crackling said, 'you've still got all your own teeth. But with that grey wig on, and those tatty clothes, you still look like a batty old tart.'

'All the better to collect Grandma's pension cheque and not have to show up for school,' little Kylie shouted triumphantly and slammed the door. She went back inside, turned on the television and watched Oprah Winfrey all afternoon.

The lawyer used his fees to invest in short time residential units and a Walt Disney theme park in the forest, right opposite where the prince and princess lived. Distraught after the disappearance of their only daughter, and driven crazy by the noise and the parking problems caused by the massive redevelopment over the road, the prince committed suicide and the princess drank herself to death.

MORAL:

Life is like a box of chocolates: the nice ones go first and all you've got left at the end is the crap

THE BARN DANCE

ONE DAY THE CHICKENS on a certain farm decided to have a party. You guessed it, a hen party.

'But how will we let all the other animals know about the show, so they can come too?' one of the chickens said.

'We could put an ad in the classifieds in *Farmer's Weekly*,' a bantam suggested.

'That's no good,' the rooster pointed out. 'Our target market – C4 pigs and upwardly mobile Hereford Shorthorns – buy the *Mirror*.'

'What about a co-ordinated TV and radio campaign using Kylie Minogue and Gazza with bumper stickers in every leading newspaper?' another of the hens suggested.

'Only if we can get Alan Parker to direct,' the rooster said. 'And he's in Ethiopia making a fifteen-second advert for a new kind of tampon.'

'In that case,' another of the hens said, 'why don't we just paint BIG PARTY TONIGHT on the rear end of a horse and get him to ride around the district? Then everyone will know about it.'

The hens ran it past each other once more, and decided it was a great concept, and so that's what they did. The party was a huge success and the horse won an award.

MORAL:

You don't have to be a horse's arse to work in the advertising business, but it helps

THE PRINCE,
THE KINDLY TINKER
AND THE INTROVERT

ONCE UPON ANOTHER TIME there was a great Russian liner offering cheap transatlantic cruises. Two days into its maiden voyage it hit an ice cube and sank. The all-Russian crew jumped into the only lifeboat and sailed off, and the only survivors from first class were a Prince and a Kindly Tinker (who was only in first class because he had just won the Pools).

Together they also managed to save the shipboard Introvert, who could not swim but was too shy and repressed to call for help.

They kept his head above the water for an hour and swam with him to a nearby island.

'Gee whiz, I'll never forget you guys,' the Introvert said. 'No one has ever been this kind to me before.'

Soon after, a lucky fairy was swimming by the island when she was attacked by a shark. (This is a fairy story; it doesn't have to be believable.) The Prince, the Kindly Tinker and the Introvert managed to save her too by linking hands and pulling the lucky fairy out of the water. So the fairy, by tradition, had to give them three wishes.

But since it was a joint venture, she only gave them one wish each.

So the Prince said, 'For my wish, I'd like you to send me back to my enchanted castle and my beautiful princess, who happens to look like Michelle Pfeiffer, and my four hundred servants, who cater to my every whim.'

And whoosh! he was gone.

'For my wish,' the Kindly Tinker said, 'I'd like you to send me back to my tinker's hut, deep in the forest, where I keep my collection of hardcore pornography, my inflatable sheep and my Nude Firemen calendar.'

(For the Kindly Tinker wasn't all that he seemed.)

And whoosh! he was gone.

Then the fairy turned to the Introvert. 'And what would you like for your wish?'

The Introvert bit his lip. 'Gee whiz, I'm starting to feel pretty lonely. I think I'd like my two new friends back.'

MORAL:

Be kind to those less fortunate than yourself – and you'll never get rid of the bastards

THE EMPRESS'S
NEW SUMMER RANGE

 NOT THAT MANY YEARS AGO there was a famous Empress who was so obsessed with image and clothes that she thought about little else. She spent almost the entire gross national product of her kingdom on Elle MacPherson Intimates and dresses from Isaac Mizrahi, Nicole Farhi and Georgio Armani. And she would have lived happily ever after but reality kept getting in the way.

Then one day two rogues came to the kingdom. Their names were Siimon and Vincente and they both had designer ponytails and wrap-around sunglasses and said they were fashion designers and exporters. They told the Empress they made very special garments that would only look good to people who were sophisticated, sexy, crazy, cool and had a lot of money.

'That sounds like me,' the Empress told herself. And she gave them a big heap of dosh to start work on a new summer range for her immediately.

So Siimon and Vincente set up their looms in her castle's east wing and pretended to start work. In fact they did no work at all. Instead they did lunch, spent hours walking around showrooms looking at imported German sporthorses and went to parties with lots of other milliners so they could have their photographs taken for glossy fashion magazines like *Renaissance, Prince* and *Wimple.*

Finally the Empress became impatient and asked them when they would be bringing her her new summer clothes. So Siimon and Vincente cobbled together a lampshade, some tin foil, some offcuts from the Bayeux tapestry, an impaling spike and three yards of red carpet and held a private fashion show for the Empress.

'This is total shit,' the Empress thought when she saw the clothes, but she did not express this thought aloud because she did not want Siimon and Vincente to think she was not sophisticated and crazy and sexy and cool.

'Isn't it marvellous?' Siimon asked her, as a mannikin came clanking along the catwalk. She was a blonde peasant wench who had been starving in the dungeons for the last six months.

'It expresses your individuality,' Vincente told her. 'It definitely makes a *statement.*'

'Absolutely,' the Empress said, and smiled most graciously.

And so the Empress wore one of the dresses to the opening of the new state thumbscrew.

'Holy Christ,' the Prime Minister thought, when he saw it, but he didn't want to be thought of as middle income and unhip so he clapped his hands and shouted; 'Fantastic!'

When the Empress strode into the audience chamber all conversation stopped. All the courtiers stared at her in stunned disbelief. But none of them wanted to show the others that they were not hip and upper-middle income so they all murmured their approval.

And as she was borne through the streets of the capital all the Empress's subjects applauded her new summer range. Except for one little boy. As she passed by he pointed to the Empress and shouted, 'Who's that fat slag in the stupid dress?'

Well, at that point the Empress freaked and had the child and his entire family burned at the stake. No one dared say a word to her after that.

And Siimon and Vincente bought a chain of *haute couture* boutiques in London, Paris, Milan and Avalon and lived snappily ever after.

MORAL:

You can lead a clothes-horse to
an exporter but you cannot
make her think

THE HUMBLE, HORNY PEASANT

ONCE UPON A TIME a humble peasant was walking through the woods when he heard someone calling.

'Help! Help!' a soft little voice yelled.

At first the man could not think where such a sound might be coming from, it was so soft, but so urgent. Then he looked down and saw a little fairy trapped on a thorn.

'Please help me,' the little fairy pleaded.

'What's in it for me?' the peasant said, being a typical man.

'If you set me free I'll grant whatever wish your heart desires,' the fairy said.

'In that case, consider it done,' he said, unhooking the little fairy and setting her on the ground.

'Thank you, kind sir,' the fairy said. 'Now, to keep my part of the verbal contract, I shall grant you one wish. Think carefully.'

'Great,' the man said. And he thought about what one thing he wanted above anything else. Being a man, he didn't have to think too long. 'I want to be hard twenty-four hours a day, and get all the ass I'll ever want,' he said.

'Very well then,' the little fairy said, and she turned him into a toilet seat.

MORAL:
*There is no such thing
as safe sex*

THE BLACK KNIGHT AND THE INTERIOR DECORATOR

 ONCE UPON A TIME, in the days when men were men and sheep were nervous, there was a handsome young knight called Jason the Aesthete. He had grown tired of jousting and sitting at round tables at Crusade Fund Raising Committees, and had no interest whatever in rescuing damsels in distress. He was more interested in doing things with his hands, in a creative sense.

So one day he set out on a gallant quest to become an interior designer.

He rode forth on his white charger, this rather stark colour offset by a quite nice cerise blanket and a pale mauve saddle – which made a strong statement, he felt – and went around the kingdom, redesigning castles, making fabulous angular tables instead of the more conventional round ones, doing some interesting things with turrets and some startling things with velour.

However, you must remember that this was the Dark Ages, and he had to tolerate some very retro behaviour. For instance, one day as he left the king's court, he found that someone had painted his horse's balls pink.

Furious, he marched back into the great hall, and shouted, 'Who just painted my horse's balls pink?'

From the midst of the crowd the largest, hairiest, ugliest knight Jason the Aesthete had ever seen stepped forward. He had a six-inch scar running along his cheek, and had only one eye. He was almost seven foot tall, and his armour, his beard, his hair and his teeth were all jet black. From the scabbard on his hip he drew the largest, heaviest, meanest-looking broadsword anyone had ever seen. It was made of blue Toledo steel and glinted like a razor.

'I, the Black Prince, painted your horse's balls pink,' he said. 'Why?'

And Jason replied, 'First coat's dry.'

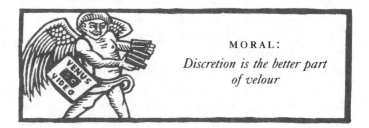

MORAL:

Discretion is the better part of velour

THE POOR CHURCH MOUSE

ONCE UPON A TIME there was a poor church mouse. He lived quietly and simply in a hole in the stone wall of an old country church, behind the vestry cupboard. No one ever bothered him and the church was always quiet. There were rarely any people around, even during the Sunday morning services, except once when the BBC showed up to record 'Hymns of Praise' and the entire south-east of England tried to get seats in the front pews.

Everyone liked the little mouse. The other rodents who lived in the churchyard never had a bad word to say about him and even the cat left him alone. Occasionally his cousin, a city mouse, would come to stay for a weekend away from his hectic life in the city, which consisted mainly of raves, dropping Ecstasy, shouting into mobile phones, and trading in currency futures. City Mouse would drive down in his Mercedes convertible and drink all Poor Church Mouse's beer, eat all his cheese – he complained if it wasn't French – and talk to him about investment opportunities.

'This is the life,' City Mouse said, putting his front paws behind his head and his back paws up on the furniture. 'I think I might get a weekender down here. I've been looking at a little place in the presbytery, behind the kitchen stove. We could rent it out when we're not using it, and the way the mouse population is expanding, in a few years' time we could chew two more holes in the skirting board and sell it as a triplex.'

But one day Church Mouse had an unbelievable run of bad luck. The church was burned down when the verger, after having a quiet smoke in the vestry, forgot to stub out his cigarette properly and all the vestments caught fire. Church Mouse was informed by his insurance company that his policy did not cover damage caused by vergers. Then he lost his entire life savings on the futures contract which his cousin had said would yield a one hundred per cent profit in ninety days. Finally, the last straw, his wife was eaten by the cat.

Poor Church Mouse felt very sorry for himself and so he went to see the other rodents who lived in the churchyard, and asked them for a loan. None of them gave a rat's. So he went to the city, to see his cousin, City Mouse. City Mouse told him that speculating in Deutschmarks was a high-risk business and to take his losses on the chin instead of whining about it. Was he man or mouse?

Finally, in desperation, he went to see the cat about compensation, and the cat ate him too.

MORAL:
If you're looking for sympathy,
it's in the dictionary between
shit and syphilis

THE COMPUTER THAT
KNEW EVERYTHING

ONCE UPON A TIME there was a boy called Nigel, whose father was a famous train-spotter. He was, like, a really amazing and technologically gifted person who used to spend all day in his room downloading computer games onto his Apple Mac or buying and selling memory banks and hard disk drives through the local community newspaper. He would sit up all night surfing the Net so he could tell other Net users about all the really amazing stuff he'd just found on the Net. But after a while – about fifteen years – he got tired with this way of life and decided to do something different.

At first he thought he'd build his own virtual reality machine, but he didn't know what reality was so he wasn't able to simulate it. So he decided to build a computer so vast, so complex and so sophisticated that it knew the answer to everything. He originally made it to design a new type of anorak but then he had the even better idea of using it to discover the meaning of life.

He fed into it all the information it requested about the pursuit of happiness and truth, like the Sermon on the Mount, the teachings of Mohammed and Buddha and how long it takes the average typist from Telford to get legless on sangria and score with a Spanish waiter on a six-day package deal to Ibiza.

When it was finally done, he asked the computer for the meaning of life.

He was so delighted with the answer that he asked the computer to send a copy of it to everyone in the whole world, so that everyone could understand what their lives were about.

Instead, the computer sent out final Poll Tax demands to every household in each town in Britain starting with a 'B', rescinded the single-parent allowance to everyone living in Bishop's Stortford, sent forms to everyone over the age of twenty-three in Swaziland demanding an income tax return for the year ended June 30th, 1957, lost the entire records of the Romanian Traffic Licensing Department and launched a pre-emptive nuclear strike on Barbados.

MORAL:

To err is human.
To really stuff up takes a
computer

THE UGLY GERBIL

'There once was an ugly gerbil,
with fur all matted and brown
and all the other gerbils
in so many verbals,
said – "SQUEAK! Get out of town!
SQUEAK! Get out! SQUEAK, SQUEAK! Get out!
SQUEAK, SQUEAK! Get out of town!"'

 SO THE UGLY GERBIL decided to seek his fame and fortune in Hollywood. His mother warned him about the dangers before he left – she even told him, in detail, about safe sex and about gerbiling, which is very *un*safe sex if you happen to be a gerbil – but he wouldn't listen.

'I have a dream,' he said.

And so he went to find his dreams in Hollywood and ended up in a pet shop on Ventura Boulevard. The other gerbils in the cage gave him a hard time because he was so ugly but he just gave them the finger – or claw, rather – and told them this was Hollywood, the place where all dreams were made. It didn't matter if he was ugly. Look at Danny de Vito.

'Yeah, but he's smart and talented,' they said. 'It's much easier to be Keanu Reeves.'

But the ugly gerbil would not be persuaded. He told them about his dream. One day he would be the pet of a famous film star, he said. He would have beautiful starlets pick him up and stroke his fur. He would live in a neon cage with a little gilt and chrome hutch to sleep in and have the straw changed by the butler every half an hour. He would press his nose against the wire mesh as multi-million dollar deals were made. He would watch Cindy Crawfords and Demi Moores stepping naked from jacuzzis. He would listen to people talking passionately about Tibet.

'No, you won't,' the other gerbils told him. 'You'll end up in a backyard garage like the rest of us, in a crumbly old wooden box with three-week-old straw and an exercise area the size of Sting's bald spot. No film star would ever want you as a pet. You're ugly.'

But the Ugly Gerbil held on to his dream and one day his dream came true. A famous film star did come into the shop and, of all the gerbils on display, he chose him.

Then he took him home, cut off his claws, put him in a condom and stuck him up his bum.

MORAL:
At the end of every rainbow there's a crock of shit

GOLDILOCKS AND THE TYPICAL NUCLEAR FAMILY

 ONCE UPON A TIME there were three bears. They all corresponded to archetypes: Papa Bear was the big one with the deep voice who supported Margaret Thatcher and Pat Buchanan, was pro-life, and liked shooting ducks; Mama Bear who was actually pro-abortion but kept her thoughts to herself; and Baby Bear was small and cute and nauseating.

One day Mama Bear, as usual, allowed herself to be exploited by the dominant males in the family by making them all a bowl of porridge for breakfast. But Papa Bear and Baby Bear said the porridge was too hot – nothing was ever good enough for them – and they went out, slamming the door behind them. Mama Bear rushed after them, shouting that she'd make them pancakes if they'd prefer.

While they were all away a young girl drove past in her daddy's red Saab. She was young, she had long golden hair and a beautiful figure, and she thought the whole world revolved around her. So when she saw the door to the cottage was unlocked she stopped the car, got out and walked straight in.

She saw some porridge on the table, so she tried some. But it wasn't bran oatmeal, and anyway it was so hot she burned her tongue, so she threw a tantrum and threw the whole lot on the floor. Then she sat in one of the chairs but a nail sticking out of the wooden seat snagged her new Chanel Lycra-mix stockings so she threw another tantrum and smashed all the furniture.

All this really wore her out so she went upstairs for a sleep, but the beds were all too hard. She wasn't used to not getting everything just the way she wanted so she really got mad and set fire to the house.

Just then the three bears came back. And Mama Bear saw Goldilocks getting into her car and shouted, 'That bitch set fire to our house!'

But Goldilocks winked at Baby Bear and gave Papa Bear a playful squeeze on the butt and breathed, 'Oh, boys, you don't believe a girl like me would do something like that, do you?'

'Of course not,' they both said, and turning to Mama Bear, said: 'It's all your fault, you must have left the stove on.'

And Goldilocks drove off, and lived happily ever after. Well actually, she was only really happy until she was thirty. After that she had to rely on face lifts and Prozac.

MORAL:

If you're young, blonde and you've got big tits, you can get away with anything

THE PERFECT MATCH

 ONCE UPON A TIME there was a young man called Barry. He was a trainee bailiff from Southend who was interested in skiing, hang-gliding, meeting people and generally having a good time, even though he'd never actually done any of these things. She was a beautiful princess called Desiree, who masqueraded as a trainee mailing clerk for a multi-national conglomerate. She liked trying on new clothes, giggling a lot and generally having fun.

Fate and television brought them together on a top rating dating programme. The show's computer gave them a compatibility rating of ninety-eight per cent, since they had the combined intelligence of an aardvark.

After the show they went off for a dirty weekend at a new high-rise resort outside Marbella at the television station's expense. They bonked each other silly the first night but the next morning, once the effects of the duty free alcohol had worn off, they found they couldn't stand the sight of each other. So Desiree spent the rest of the week in bed being lanced by a former picador.

However, when they got back the TV show's producer, worried about a drop in the ratings, persuaded them to get married on air. Seduced by the offer of an all-expenses-paid wedding – they didn't want to get married but they couldn't say no to anything that was free – they agreed. So shortly afterwards they were married in a simple but moving ceremony on the seventeenth-floor balcony of Desiree's family home in Chingford.

They started breeding like rabbits, hoping to use the accrued family benefit to save for a home in Barking. Eventually they had eight children who seemed to spend all their time shouting, eating, watching television and vomiting on the carpet.

Just like their father.

Desiree decided she couldn't stand it any longer, especially as they still had only £4.63 saved towards the house in Barking. She tried to commit suicide by watching videos of Germaine Greer over and over. It wasn't enough to kill her but it did put her in intensive care for a month.

Her case received in-depth coverage in the national media – almost four lines in the *Sun*. The television executive who had produced the dating programme was now in charge of current affairs at ITN and he decided to use Barry and Desiree in a fly-on-the-wall documentary about Britain's underclass.

During forty minutes of filming at Barry and Desiree's flat the cameras recorded the delivery of seven takeaway pizzas, the arrival of two detectives who questioned Barry about the theft of a video recorder in Romford, and an argument which ended when Barry strangled Desiree with his West Ham scarf. The crew decided not to intervene in an effort to preserve the artistic integrity of their work.

Desiree's sister sued the television company on behalf of the children, who were awarded eight million pounds in damages. Two weeks later she took all the money and went to live in Marbella with the producer.

MORAL:
It's better to have loved and lost.
Much better

THE PRINCESS AND THE FROG

ONCE UPON A TIME a beautiful princess was walking through the forest. As she reached a large pond in the middle of a cool glade she heard a voice saying, 'Hey, spunky! Over here!'

She looked up and was amazed to see a tiny green frog looking at her. 'Kermit?' she said, surprised.

'No, my name's Galahad,' the frog said. 'A wicked witch put a spell on me. Come and suck face with me and I'll turn into a handsome prince.'

Well, the princess did. She sucked and sucked but nothing happened. Finally the little frog bounced away.

'Where's the handsome prince?' the princess cried.

'Sorry, Babe,' the frog said. 'Look . . . er . . . I'll call you, OK?'

The princess was very disappointed. Every day she came to the forest and waited by the pond and each day a different frog appeared and the same thing happened. Years passed and the princess had all but given up hope when finally she sucked face with one of the frogs and it actually *did* turn into a handsome prince.

'At last,' she said, 'now we can live happily ever after.'

'Well actually, Honey,' the handsome prince said,

spitting green slime out of his mouth, 'first you'll have to do something about your breath. You smell like a frog. Look, er . . . I'll call you, OK?'

But one day, we are happy to report, the princess kissed another frog. And although he still looked like a frog, he did turn out to be a prince. They got married and she lived in constant public scrutiny ever afterwards, was hassled by tabloid journalists who took photos of her in bikinis seven months pregnant and made comments about the size of her thighs. She had her character and private life dissected in the daily newspapers and ended up divorced and in therapy.

MORAL:
A girl has to suck a lot of horny toads before she finds her handsome prince. And even then there are no guarantees

WOMEN FOR
TRANSMOGRIFICATION

ONCE UPON A TIME there was a little girl called Cinderella. Her mother was going to call her Love Peace Harmony Understanding Stephen Stills Haight-Ashbury Woodstock, but decided against it, because the people next door had called their baby that.

Cinderella's mother was married to her father, but her father was married to an advertising agency. He was called Marcus, even by his friends. A few months after Cinderella was born her mother ran off to live on a commune in Wales with Marcus's secretary, a sensitive and very caring man called Simon, whom everyone mistook for a homosexual because he didn't like football. And Marcus was left with Cinderella and three days of client contact reports to type up.

For a long time he was very sad and bitter and lonely, but then, two days later, he brought home Rosemary, a client who owned a chain of fashion stores. He rogered her in the newly decorated upstairs bedroom with the Japanese screens, thus cementing the account and the bedsheets at the same time.

The next day he took her to a little North Italian restaurant he knew about in Covent Garden that was only open the third Wednesday of every second month between three and five p.m. during leap years, where the *fettucine al pesto* has to be tasted to be believed. There, Marcus and the fashion store account related on a deep and meaningful level and Marcus proposed to her over the third bottle of Frascati.

A week later they were married in a brief garden ceremony they had written themselves during a brainstorming session with the agency's creative department. The ceremony began with an animated sausage telling the congregation that Marcus was a bit of an animal and ended with the celebrant giving a personal endorsement of the marriage concept.

The reception was a small and typically restrained affair, with the men standing around the jeroboam discussing their investment portfolios and the women in the kitchen doing pelvic floor exercises while they swapped recipes for getting rid of stretchmarks.

Rosemary brought with her her three daughters from a previous marriage. The girls all looked a little like their father, which was unfortunate, as he happened to be a Scottish builder with a broken nose and a body like a bank safe. He had outlived his usefulness years before when Rosemary's second-hand dress shop became a fashion boutique. In an out-of-court settlement she won half the concrete he had ever poured.

Everything went well for Marcus and Rosemary until the stock market crashed and Marcus lost everything he held dear: his money, his shares, and his faith in insider trading. He also lost the few hundred thou he had set aside to pay his tax bill and so he did the only honourable thing: he skipped the country and went to live in the Virgin Islands.

So it was that when poor Cinders grew up she found herself living in a council house in Walthamstow that was little but not at all charming, with her stepmother and three ugly sisters, who had grown up to look like gargoyles in brown wind-cheaters.

The three sisters all had crew cuts and wore dungarees. They were very supportive of each other and believed in networking principles. Each of the three sisters despised money, men and beauty.

The feeling was mutual.

The three ugly sisters were very unkind to poor Cinderella. They made her wear brown overalls and shave her head and go with them to see deep and meaningful French documentaries in a Notting Hill cinema.

One day Cinderella heard that there was going to be a dance at an inner London boys' school, and any pubescent girls over the age of twelve were invited. Cinderella was very excited. It was her opportunity to meet someone who might become one of the bastions of society, like a lawyer or judge or an international drug dealer. Cinderella had always dreamed of driving a Ferrari and double parking it in Curzon Street or perhaps even getting to know someone who had been involved in scandal on the front page of the *Sun*. This was her big chance.

Her sisters had a deep and meaningful discussion about the dance and decided to go. Well, not actually go inside, they were planning on hanging around the car park, pouring enamel paint on a few Mercs and shouting 'Women for Transmogrification!' at anyone going inside.

Cinderella asked if she could go with them.

'Certainly not!' one of the sisters shrieked. 'You'll only end up meeting someone who will want to manipulate you and make you a sort of female slave for the rest of your life. No, you're better off staying at home and doing the washing-up.'

'And making our beds,' another of the sisters added.

'And cooking lentil rissoles,' the third sister said.

So that night poor little Cinders was left all alone. She sat on the recliner Marcus had used for dreaming up creative concepts for toilet rolls, and big tears ran down her cheeks and sploshed onto her sisters' collection of healing crystals.

Suddenly she heard the sound of someone jemmying open one of the windows and a voice gasp, 'Oh, Ker-ist, Norman, I thought you said they'd all gone out!'

Cinderella looked up in surprise. 'Are you my fairy godmother?' she asked.

'Do I look like anybody's fairy godmother?' the intruder said, mincing into the room in a tight pair of profiterole brown Armani trousers, a fettucine yellow Pierre Charbonnier blouson shirt and a cabernet-sauvignon coloured Gianni Versace jacket.

Frankly, the answer was yes. But instead Cinderella said, 'If you're not my fairy godmother what are you doing here?'

'I've come to steal the video, darling. My name's Jeremy, and this is my friend, Norman.'

Yuppers looked around and saw Norman. He was wearing an SS cap and a black leather jacket. He had more chains wrapped around him than a beer fridge at an Alcoholics Anonymous convention.

Norman took one look at Cinders and said, 'Shall we tie her up?'

'Tie her up?' Jeremy squealed. 'What for? You aren't going to call the police, are you, dear?'

'Well maybe not tie her up,' Norman said, 'but we could tie her *down*. After all, she does look a bit like a boy.'

When he said that, Cinderella started to cry. And Jeremy, who was a sensitive and caring person, started to cry too.

'What's the matter with you two?' Norman said irritably.

'I don't want to look like a boy,' she said. 'I want to look like a girl.'

'So do I,' Jeremy cried.

'I don't want to be independent and self-assured,' Cinders sobbed. 'I want to sit in hairdressing salons and read *Cosmopolitan* while my hair is teased by an Italian man with a gold bracelet and a chest wig.'

'So do I,' Jeremy cried.

'Life sucks,' she said.

'So do I,' Jeremy cried.

By now Norman had unplugged the video and started to clank up the hallway to the front door. 'Are you coming or what?' he said to Jeremy.

'You always say that,' Jeremy said. 'I wish you'd take your time for once. We can't leave this poor little thing like this.'

'Look,' Norman said, 'it's only a cheap Korean brand. The insurance will pay for it.'

'Perhaps we could just take her pocket calculator and clock-radio instead,' Jeremy said.

'I don't care about the video or the clock-radio!' Cinderella shouted. 'I just want to go to the dance. But I can't go looking like this!'

Jeremy felt so sorry for poor Cinders when he heard her story that he insisted on taking her home instead of the VCR. Then he got to work and made her a new latex dress out of one of Norman's old dungeon outfits. He lent her his purse and the blonde wig he had bought especially for a Pet Shop Boys concert.

And Norman even offered to lend her his pink convertible Volkswagen.

'You've both been so wonderful,' Cinders cried. 'What can I ever do to repay you?'

'Just make sure you have the car back before twelve o'clock tomorrow,' Norman said. 'We've got an appointment at the clinic at one thirty.'

Cinderella promised, and off she drove to the dance. Almost immediately she let herself get hit on by the son of a leading arms dealer and Conservative politician. She and her new boyfriend did some prohibited substances, then dodged out the back to avoid the *Sun* photographers and drove off in one of his father's Aston Martins.

His parents had a townhouse in Mayfair and that night there was no one home. His father was in Brussels on an EEC junket and his mother was at Balmoral having a quickie with Prince Charles. Cinderella was overjoyed. She had finally arrived. She was part of the Establishment.

The boy, who would only give his name as Master X, showed her around the house, pointing out the Monets and the helipad and the crates of Semtex. Then they sat in the hot tub drinking magnums of Laurent Perrier Cuvée Grand Siècle and inter-relating on a deep and meaningful level by sliding their toes up and down each other's genitals.

Cinders enjoyed herself so much she forgot all about the time. When she woke up the next morning she found herself in the master bedroom with Master X sprawled naked next to her, empty bottles and bits of powdered substances all over the floor.

When she walked out onto the balcony the smog had turned a milky yellow so she knew it must be morning. She shouted down to an agent from HM Customs who was exercising in the pool and asked him the time. He peered at his gold Piaget and told her it was five minutes before noon.

Five before noon! She had promised Norman that she would bring his car back before twelve o'clock. She threw on her clothes and ran out of the apartment so fast she forgot her purse. She caught a cab back to the college only to discover that one of her three sisters had poured enamel paint onto the Volkswagen and urinated on the tyres. Embarrassed, she left the car outside Jeremy's place with the wig and the latex dress, knocked on the door, and ran.

Then poor little Cinders made her way back home where she discovered that Rosemary had taken her non-appearance at breakfast as confirmation that she had been brutally murdered by a knife-wielding sex maniac and was already breaking down on camera for ITN news. In fact she was enjoying herself so much she refused to acknowledge that Cinders was who she said she was, and had one of the three ugly sisters take her out to the back shed and do her in with a weeding fork to keep her quiet.

Meanwhile Master X had woken up to find Cinderella gone. He was heartbroken. There wasn't even a wet patch for him to remember her by. He thought he had lost her for ever, but then he looked down and saw her purse lying by the side of the bed.

He picked it up, pocketed the loose change and searched through the contents until he found an invoice for '*leather goods, various, with bonus lash*' with Jeremy's address at the top.

'Cinderella!' Master X whispered.

That afternoon he parked the Aston Martin outside Jeremy's absolutely darling little terraced house with the duck-egg blue walls. Jeremy answered the door wearing the wig and the latex dress, and was absolutely thrilled when Master X gave him a big kiss on the lips.

'Cinderella!' Master X shouted.

'I'm not Cinderella,' Jeremy said, confused.

'You look like Cinderella,' Master X said, 'and there's one sure way to prove you are. Cinders left her purse behind and it had her vibrator in it. Whoever fits the vibrator is the girl of my dreams.'

And so Master X inserted the vibrator into Jeremy, who didn't seem to mind a bit, and of course it fitted perfectly. (Because it was Jeremy's vibrator.)

'Cinderella!' Master X shouted over the buzzing noise.

'If you say so,' Jeremy said.

And so Jeremy and Master X became an item and they lived comfortably off the proceeds of the armaments business and were blissfully happy – for about two weeks. Then Mister X got back from Brussels and found out his son was living with a fruit. Mister X felt this liaison reflected unfavourably on him as a gangster and a member of parliament and so poor Jeremy ended up at the bottom of the Thames intimately attached to a concrete vibrator.

Mister X went on to become a member of the cabinet and feature regularly in the usual scandals. Norman, heartbroken by Jeremy's betrayal, went queer and started going round with girls. One day he met the three ugly sisters at Aldershot, where they were protesting against the war, even though there wasn't one, and he pinched one of them on the bum. Incensed, they chained him to a copy of the London phone directory (using his own chains) and threw him in the river near where they had dumped Cinders. And, having got away with two murders, they decided they had hidden talents in this area and became professional hitmen (not hitpersons, because only men are violent). They made a lot of money at it and became respectable members of the community.

MORAL:
Life is like a shit sandwich –
the more bread you got,
the less shit you gotta eat

THE MAN OF
UNCOMMON FAITH

 THERE WAS ONCE a very saintly man who believed that God was the answer to everything. He would go round from house to house, knocking on doors, trying to sell people magazines about how God so loveth people who go round knocking on doors, and bearing witness unto Him. He also visited unto people that were sick and toldeth them it was their own fault because they did not believe in Him enough and he madeth them prayeth with him. And he told people who had lost their jobs or lost their husbands or wives, or were depressed, or unhappy, or could not make their computers work, that if they believeth in God enough everything would be all right. And everyone reveredeth this man, because the world just loveth a quick and easy fix more than anything else, especially if it discounteth them of all responsibility.

And one day this man was walking along the street, clapping his hands and singing songs in praise of the Lord, when a mugger steppeth out from a street corner and sayeth to the goodly man, 'Give me your wallet, turkey, or I'll spread you all over the footpath.'

And the goodly man replied, saying, 'Lo, all that I hath is mine. But if thou will repent, and giveth up thy sinning ways, I will giveth you a copy of this magazine, for a small donation.'

And so the mugger breaketh his cheekbone.

But the goodly man simply got up and offereth the mugger his other cheek, as it sayeth in the Bible, and the mugger breaketh that one too. And then he bendeth the goodly man over a parking metre and inserteth a part of a bus stop up him.

MORAL:

Blessed are the meek –
it gives the rest of us a
better chance

THE POUND OF FLESH

 ONCE UPON ANOTHER TIME there was a man named Bassiano, who, as you can tell by the name, almost certainly had drug and mafia connections. He needed money urgently to invest in what he believed was an excellent business opportunity, but none of the banks would look at him, probably because he was an undischarged bankrupt currently on bail charged with being the accomplice in an armed robbery case.

Now at about that time there lived a Jew by the name of Shylock, who was in the business of lending money at extravagant interest rates. Bassiano asked Shylock for a loan of two thousand ducats, just till his ship came in. Shylock agreed to loan him the money, at ten per cent interest per week.

'I'll pay you back,' Bassiano shouted, putting the money in his purse and skipping happily away.

'Be sure you do,' Shylock told him. 'No matter what happens, I always get my pound of flesh.'

Three months went by and Shylock had still not received any repayments on the loan, so he went looking for Bassiano. He found him in an alleyway behind a pub in Notting Hill Gate, which was rather unusual, as he lived in Venice.

'Where's the vig on the two thousand ducats?' Shylock asked him.

'I don't have it right at this moment,' Bassiano answered. 'My business opportunity came in last.'

'I need the juice.'

Bassiano shrugged. 'You can't get blood out of a stone,' he said.

'Like I said, I still want my pound of flesh,' Shylock said, and he took it, using a chainsaw and a rather large cut-throat razor.

As a result of this action Bassiano was later found dead in the boot of a car parked behind a warehouse in sixteenth-century Venice, near the Piazza San Marco.

When she heard what had happened, Bassiano's friend, Portia, dressed herself up as a lawyer's clerk and hastened to the Court of Justice. But while a date for the trial was being fixed – both the prosecution and the defence teams had a lot of trouble finding jurors who had not already read about the case at school – Portia grew quickly to love the law. She enjoyed having investment portfolios, driving fast gondolas and having houses in Constantinople and Aquitaine. So instead of seeking justice for her friend Bassiano she did what any reasonable barrister would do, she decided to set up her own expensive law practice. Soon afterwards Shylock retained her as his defence counsel, at five hundred ducats a day plus expenses.

When the case finally got to court Portia argued that Bassiano and Shylock had had a verbal contract for the pound of flesh and that Shylock was perfectly entitled to it. She appealed to the jury to consider Shylock's deprived childhood which had left him traumatised and said that society must take the blame for his actions. She harped on about the fact that Shylock was Jewish, and alleged that the case was inspired by racism and played the jurors a tape that she said proved one of the Doge's soldiers was anti-Semitic. She destroyed the prosecution's main witness – Shylock's own daughter, Jessica – by implying that her testimony was motivated by greed, and that she stood to inherit a great deal of money if her father was executed by the State.

In the end she had Shylock acquitted on a technicality, and helped him sell the movie and book rights for his story to a Hollywood film studio. She became rich and famous and lived happily ever after.

MORAL:

What is the difference between a lawyer and a catfish? One is a bottom-dwelling, scum-eating little shark, and a catfish . . . is just a catfish

THE GIANT AND THE BOY
WITH THE CATAPULT

ONCE THERE WAS a fearsome giant called Goliath, but everyone called him Fats. You know the sort of bloke; sold drugs, rode a Harley Davidson, played music too loud, burned rubber in the street at four o'clock in the morning and generally didn't give a shit.

One day the Israelites, who were a family of Jews living right next door to Fats, got together and said, 'OK, we need a volunteer to knock on the door and ask him to turn his stereo down.'

And David, who was the youngest and smallest of the family and so always felt he had something to prove, said, 'I'll do it.'

And everyone laughed.

But David was determined. He fetched his catapult and went outside and shouted over the fence, 'Hey, dickhead! Shut it down or you'll be eating lunch through a tube!'

Fats came out in his black AC/DC T-shirt, the sleeves rolled up past his third tattoo, and said, 'Are you looking for a stompin', short arse?'

And David said, 'Come and try it, penis breath.'

So Fats came over and David pulled out his catapult

and cracked Fats right around the scone with a half brick.

Well, as anyone who's ever smacked a biker over the head with anything less than a combine harvester knows, it didn't do bugger all good. Fats grabbed David by the throat, rearranged his sinuses and other pieces of anatomical structure and did wheelies on his face with his Harley Davidson. And David spent the next six months in intensive care and had to have his catapult surgically removed.

MORAL:

The bigger they are,
the faster you run

THE KINDLY BEAR AND THE FOX

ONCE THERE WAS a young bird which lived on the steppes of Russia. One day it was caught out in the open during a sudden blizzard. It lay on the ground, freezing to death in the snow.

Now a kindly bear happened to pass by and it picked up the small bird in its mouth. Realising the bird's predicament it placed it in some of its own fresh droppings, and moved on. The heat from the manure soon thawed out the young bird, but as soon as it got itself warm it discovered it was stuck there. So it started squawking and chirping as loud as it could.

A fox heard its cries, found the bird, pulled it out of the bear droppings, and ate it.

MORAL:

It's not always your worst enemy who drops you in the shit. It's not always your best friend who gets you out. And if you're in the shit, for God's sake, shut up about it

83

THE MOUSE AND THE LION

ONCE UPON A TIME there was a mouse with attitude. He wore his baseball cap back to front, wore his Reeboks to bed, and had thick gold chains around his neck. He had close connections with the underworld, had three priors for GBH, armed robbery and kidnapping, and a recording contract with Sony. His favourite – only – form of expression was rap.

One day he was jive-assing through the jungle when he saw a great lion caught up in a trapper's net.

'Hey dude,' the mouse said. 'What's happenin', bro'?'

'Just fuck off,' the lion said, because he was a pretty bad-tempered lion.

'Hey man, you want me to git you outta that thing?' the mouse asked. 'I am the mouse that's really grouse. The rodent of the moment. I eat cheese and I aim to please.'

'I don't give a stuff what you do,' the lion snarled.

The little mouse gnawed and gnawed at the net, and finally, four hours later, the lion was free.

'Yo, bro',' the mouse said. 'I may be poor, but I can gnaw, and I am the greatest mouse you ever saw. I'm a meece, but don't call the police ... HOLY SH—!'

The lion ate the mouse, and stomped away. Despite his incredibly lucky escape, he still growled at anyone who came near him all that day.

MORAL:

*It's better to have shit
on the liver
than rap on the brain*

THE DAMSEL IN DISTRESS

 THERE WAS ONCE a brave knight called Sir Robin the Brave. His job description involved riding about the country being gallant to women, chivalrous to men, and going to car-boot sales and auctions looking for something called the Holy Grail. Generally, it was a pretty good life.

One day, as he rode into a little hamlet, all the people rushed out of their houses to meet him and threw themselves on the ground in front of his horse, shouting, 'Thank God you're here!'

At first he thought they might need a hand with some silly bint who had fallen under a spell and needed kissing. But on further enquiry the village headman mumbled, 'It is the dragon, sire! It has stolen away my beautiful daughter and taken her up to its lair in the mountains. What are we to do?'

'Fear ye not,' the knight said, 'I was trained for situations like this.'

And he unsheathed his broadsword, which wasn't easy on a horse, as it was very broad, and he rode up the mountain to face the dragon.

When he reached the lip of the cave, he saw a wooden

stake outside. The beautiful maiden was tied to the post (though this begs the question: how did a giant lizard with only three claws and no apposable thumb tie knots in rope?) and from inside the cave came a great roaring and burning noise.

'I've come to save you from the dreadful dragon,' the knight said.

The damsel heaved her not inconsequential bosom and shouted, 'Oh, knight, you are so brave to risk disfiguring burns, crippling injuries, even a slow and agonising death for a complete stranger like me.'

The knight thought about this for a moment. 'Run that by me again?' he said.

At that moment the dragon appeared from the cave. It was a terrible beast, eighteen feet high, with razor sharp claws, terrible yellow pointed teeth, flames and smoke emerging from its nostrils, greasy green scales on its back, a powerful tail, and, if that wasn't enough, a bad case of halitosis.

The knight bravely charged up to it and with great precision threw his broadsword at the beast, striking it above the heart. But the dragon's scales were armour-plated and the sword bounced off and broke in two on the dirt.

Well, he'd given it his best shot.

The knight immediately swung his horse around and galloped back to the village.

'Did you slay the great beast?' the village headman asked.

'Well, actually, no,' the knight said. 'In fact I've

changed my mind on that, to be honest. The maiden isn't that beautiful. She probably isn't even a virgin. And I'm not sure if I agree with the culling of another species simply because they do not conform to human patterns of behaviour. After all, they say at this rate dragons will be extinct by the twentieth century, unless we do something now. And he didn't seem like such a bad dragon, as dragons go. I don't think he really intends to harm her. And I'm not in the mood. Anyway, I really wanted to be a blacksmith.'

And he rode off.

MORAL:

*If at first you don't succeed,
deny you were even trying*

SNOW WHITE AND THE SEVEN MINORITY GROUPS

ONCE UPON A TIME, long ago – in the days before Chairpersons and Affirmative Action – a gentle queen sat by his window doing macramé and eating alternative muesli. As he worked he pricked his finger so that two tiny drops of blood fell from it. He immediately went into a screaming fit, and ran to find his live-in lover, Nigel.

When the fuss had died down, two days later, the old queen sighed, and said, 'Wouldn't it be simply delish if we had a little kiddywinks with cheeks as rosy as those drops of blood, with skin as white as that coke we scored last week and hair as black as latex rubber! We could bring him up as our very own and validate our relationship.'

'Yes,' said Nigel, 'it just isn't *fair.*'

But by a miracle of modern science the old queen's wish came true and they had a little daughter. Just like the old queen's dream she had pure white skin that she later tanned brown on the Algarve, sable black hair that she dyed blonde in the King's Road, and rosy red lips that she painted blue. They called her Doreen and she grew up and got a job as an apprentice beautician but for the sake of poetic licence we shall call her Snow White.

She was sweet and lovely, and very popular with the boys because she was also upfront, laid-back, consciously aware, and the only girl in her class who didn't have Herpes II.

When Snow White was fifteen the old queen died of AIDS. Snow White's other father, Nigel, had a sex change because he didn't want Snow White to grow up without a mother. But as he, or she, or it, grew older he, she or it became extremely vain. He, she or it had a face lift, a nose job, a tummy tuck and finally a hysterectomy, despite the fact that he, she or it didn't even have a uterus. He, she or it just didn't want to be the only cross-dresser at he, she or its encounter group who hadn't had the op.

And every day when Nigel looked in the mirror he asked:

'Mirror, mirror on the wall,
who's the loosest tart of all?'

And the mirror would always answer, 'You are, you old poof.'

But as the years passed young Snow White grew even more sweet and lovely on a strict diet of bean shoots, natural yoghurt and ginseng, so that one day when Nigel asked the old, old question, the mirror replied:

'Sorry, Nige, let's face it dear,
your menopause is drawing near.'

This made the old tart so *cross*. It just wasn't *fair*.

Nigel looked at Snow White and was filled with the sort of insane, unreasoning jealousy seldom found anywhere outside of old 'Neighbours' scripts. Snow White was a constant reminder to him of the day when he, too, had a tight little bum. So Nigel rang a friend he knew from his cocaine dealing days and paid him ten grand to add Snow White to the growing list of unsolved drug-related murders around London.

The man befriended Snow White in a bar and took her off into Epping Forest on some transparent pretext, planning to ice her and bury her in a shallow grave, like he'd seen them do on television.

But Snow White wasn't as dumb as she looked. She'd actually been doing a little work on the side at nights, giving personal massage to visiting Japanese and Arab business executives, and she had some money saved up. She offered the man another ten grand to let her live on the condition that she disappear for ever.

The kindly contract killer agreed to this and instead wasted a lonely and overweight amateur ornithologist who had wandered into the forest searching for a Lesser Spotted Night Shriek.

Left alone, poor Snow White wandered about in the forest until she came to a little mock-colonial cottage. She opened the door and went in. Inside she found seven beds, seven plates of wholemeal spaghetti and seven sets of the Collected Works of Nathan Pritikin. She ate one of the books in preference to the wholemeal spaghetti and then, her vitamin B reserves already depleted after her stressful encounter with the contract killer, she lay down on one of the Japanese futons and went to sleep.

Now the cottage had been rented out by seven members of various minority groups. Their names were Shorty, Darky, Greeny, Lefty, Slopey, Julian and Lesley. When it was dark they returned and to their surprise they found the lovely Snow White asleep.

'What a top sort,' they all said, except for Julian, for reasons that should become clear later.

'Yeah,' said Shorty, 'let's tie her to the bed and get the whips and the rubber gear,' for as everyone knows, all minorities are deviants. Just then Snow White woke up and sat up in bed in alarm.

'Who are you?' Snow White said.

'My name's Lefty,' said the radical one, who was also leader of the group. He had been elected leader when the other six had failed to show up for a committee meeting he had called in secret. 'We're all members of minority groups. As victims of society we came here to get away from systematic oppression. Who are you?'

'My name's Snow White,' she said, 'and I'm a pure-bred Anglo-Saxon. If you don't like it in this country why don't you all go back where you came from, you bunch of losers?'

'I am where I came from, bro',' said Darky. 'Besides, the lease on this place is in our name.'

They decided they would let her stay with them in return for a little basic cooking and cleaning in lieu of rent – and for a while this arrangement worked quite well. Every day the gang got up and went to work in a little gold mine. It was called New Age and it sold tapes called 'Song of the Whale' – no, not Pavarotti – and 'Green Forest' and 'Favourite Classics from Tibet'. They also sold crystals and massage oil and books on tantric yoga and environmentally friendly condoms.

After a couple of months Snow White begged them to let her come with them and help in the shop, but they insisted she stay home and make the futons.

'It just isn't *fair*,' Snow White muttered.

Snow White was bored and frustrated so she took up jogging. Every afternoon after her chores she put on her Nikes and her Puma T-shirt and her pink sweat band and jogged down to the little cave by the pool to work out, have a shower under the waterfall and shave her armpits.

'Why do you shave under your armpits?' Lesley asked her one day.

'Why not?' Snow White said.

'You realise it's just another way that women are exploited,' Lesley said. 'You're just conforming to the physiological and emotional stereotype imposed on you by the male-dominated Judaeo-Christian neo-chauvinist society.'

'No, I didn't realise that,' Snow White said, wondering what she meant.

So Lefty explained it to her in terms of the class struggle, and Darky and Slopey explained it in terms of the genocide of native populations by invading cultures, Greeny told her about the destruction of the ozone layer, Julian explained the psychology of sexual dominance and

Shorty told her how he could never get off-the-rack jeans to fit.

She learned about the exploitation of women, the historical oppression of indigenous populations, discrimination against homosexuals by the Church and State, racial bigotry, the rape of the land, the oppression of the working class by the capitalist system and how short people can't see as well at the cricket.

'It just isn't *fair*,' Shorty added.

And slowly Snow White became radicalised.

In the following weeks she learned to re-examine her value system. And she learned so well that one day she decided she no longer wanted to stay home and cook lentil and carrot pie. 'That's it,' she told them one day. 'I've had enough. No more Ms Nice Person for me. I'm going to get a job.'

'Wait a minute,' Lesley said. 'When we said women were oppressed, we didn't mean *you*. You can't do this to us.'

'No,' said Darky. 'It isn't *fair*.'

'That's life,' Snow White said and next day she got a job as a sales consultant with a real estate company. Now it just so happened that the company was owned by Nigel's latest live-in lover. One day he told Nigel about his new star salesperson and when Nigel discovered it was actually Snow White he was furious.

'If you want something done in this country,' he fumed, 'you have to do it your bloody self,' and so he started making plans to do Snow White in himself.

The next day, disguised as a property-developer –

Rolls, silver toupee, gold identity bracelet – he made a phone appointment with Snow White and drove out to see her. They went out to lunch to discuss a land deal and Nigel took her to a little Lebbo place he knew and told her there wasn't any meat in the ladies' fingers and the dressing in the tabbouleh was polyunsaturated. Snow White remembered what Slopey had told her about foreign food, but the ladies' fingers looked so crisp and appetizing and the tabbouleh was so green and fresh that she went ahead anyway and had three helpings.

And, of course, with all that cholesterol in her bloodstream, the very next day she had a massive coronary infarction and fell into a coma. It was the perfect crime. Well, if not perfect, pretty bloody good.

That evening, when the gang came home from a day at a male bonding seminar, they guessed at once what had happened. They dialled emergency and got the chiropractor round. He suggested an orthopaedic bed – but to no avail. Then they tried their iridologist, their herbalist, their acupuncturist and a man who advertised foot massage at a very reasonable rate in the local paper. They even took Snow White along to a charismatic Mass.

Nothing worked.

Finally, in desperation, they called their family doctor. He examined Snow White for two hours and left a prescription for Prozac.

Meanwhile, back in his apartment, Nigel gazed into the mirror and said:

'*Mirror, mirror, on the ceiling,*
Do I look like that, or is my tan just peeling?'

But the mirror didn't say anything because it didn't want to hurt his feelings.

Shorty and the rest of the gang finally realised all their efforts to revive Snow White were in vain. She was dead. They decided to bury her but agreed to wait until the following week as Shorty's cousin Perv was due to visit them.

Perv was a necrophiliac.

Sorrowfully they undressed her and put her in a beautiful robe. They enjoyed it so much they undressed her and put her in the beautiful robe again. Then they did it again. This went on for days. However, on the following Tuesday a young prince happened to pass that way. His name was Roger and he wasn't actually a prince. He wasn't actually all that handsome either but he had an interesting personality and he hoped to get a job in the hospitality industry.

Roger knocked on the door, trying to sell teatowels for a worthy charity, and saw Snow White asleep through the window. Checking there were no German Shepherds or security devices around, he crept inside. He hadn't scored for months – you didn't get anywhere these days without at least a BMW – and this seemed like a golden opportunity. He quickly sprayed some deodorant under his arms, leaned over, and kissed her once on the lips.

At once Snow White woke and sat bolt upright. She looked at Roger and screamed.

At that moment Shorty and the gang came home and told her the story of Nigel's wickedness and how she came to be there and how Roger had revived her from death with just one kiss.

'With just one kiss?' Snow White said.

'That's right,' said Roger.

'What an ego.'

'How about a bit of gratitude?' Roger said.

'Typical male attitude,' Snow White said, getting up and slipping on a pair of thongs. 'One kiss solves everything.'

'I want you to come with me and be my bride,' Roger said. 'We'll get a remote control video and live happily ever after.'

'No thanks.'

'But I love you,' Roger said.

'You hardly know me.'

'It doesn't matter. You're beautiful. On a scale of one to ten you must be ... well, at least a nine and a half, 'cause I don't give tens.'

'I've had enough of this,' Snow White said. 'People think of me as just a body. I have a mind too, you know.'

'All this isn't in the script,' Roger said. 'You're supposed to climb on my horse and ride off with me into the sunset.'

'A horse? You mean you don't even have a red Cordia, at the very least?' And she stalked off towards the door.

'This just isn't *fair*,' Roger said.

'Where are you going?' Shorty asked.

'I'm through with being exploited,' Snow White told

him. 'I'm going to stop wearing make-up and go back to college to do environmental studies.'

And off she went.

Shorty and the gang decided to go after her, and went to the far corners of the world – New Zealand, Greenland, Novya Zemlya, Telford – searching for her.

Darky was arrested in Queensland, Australia, spent the night in the lock-up, and was buried the next day.

Greeny was blown up aboard his yacht in Auckland Harbour.

Shorty formed a dwarf-throwing act in Canada and met with an untimely end while creating a new world record.

Julian walked into a pub in Glasgow, asked for a glass of milk, and was never heard from again.

Lefty was last seen in Santiago, getting into a car with a suspected CIA agent.

Lesley, desperate to have a child of her own, was artificially inseminated by her girlfriend's twenty-stone brother and died in childbirth.

Slopey turned out to be a short, left-handed, homosexual Mongolian Baha'i who voted SDP, and thus became one of the world's smallest minority groups. He was deported as an undesirable alien and was refused citizenship everywhere, even Uruguay, and finally died of starvation on a flight between McMurdo Sound and the Galapagos Islands.

Snow White met an upwardly mobile computer salesman, betrayed her principles and fell in love, got married, got divorced, lost the custody battle and finished up getting the children. All boys.

And Nigel? He was caught giving Hugh Grant a blow-job in the front of his Range Rover. He got off with a fifty-pound fine, sold his story to the *Daily Telegraph* and then got a sponsorship deal for a new kind of lipstick. He invested the proceeds in a theme park in Essex and lived happily ever after with Roger.

MORAL:
You're right – life really
isn't *fair*